LAWN OF DOOM

Written by **PAUL TOBIN**
Art by **RON CHAN**
Colors by **MATT J. RAINWATER**
Letters by **STEVE DUTRO**
Cover by **RON CHAN**

DARK HORSE BOOKS

PLANTS
vs.
ZOMBIES

LAWN OF DOOM

Publisher **MIKE RICHARDSON**
Senior Editor **PHILIP R. SIMON**
Associate Editor **MEGAN WALKER**
Designer **BRENNAN THOME**
Digital Art Technician **CHRISTINA McKENZIE**

Special thanks to Alexandria Land, A.J. Rathbun, Kristen Star, and everyone at PopCap Games.

Scholastic edition: August 2018
ISBN 978-1-50670-048-8

10 9 8 7 6 5 4 3 2 1
Printed in Canada

DarkHorse.com
PopCap.com

No plants were harmed in the making of this graphic novel. However, many lawns were completely destroyed and many pieces of Halloween candy were sacrificed to Nate Timely's neverending appetite.

"MY 'LOTS OF ZOMBIES JUMP OUT AND THUMP YOU ON THE HEAD' TRAP? THAT'S GOING IN A *LOT* OF LAWNS."

YES, EVERY LAWN IN NEIGHBORVILLE WILL TURN INTO A...

...LAWN OF *DOOM!!!*

"WITH THE EXCEPTION OF ONE LAWN THAT'S RESERVED FOR MR. STUBBINS BECAUSE HE WANTS TO HOLD HIS TAFFY-MAKING CONVENTION."

ZOMTAFF 3000

SQUICK!

"AND THEN THERE'S ALSO ONE LAWN FOR POP SMART SNACKS."

POP SMARTS

No Admittance ZOMBIES ONLY!!

FROGPAAANTS?

BRAINS?

SCRATCH SCRATCH

POKE

AND I'D PROBABLY BETTER RESERVE FORTY-THREE VARIOUS LAWNS FOR MEDICAL SERVICES, BECAUSE MY ZOMBIES ARE TERRIBLE AT TRIGGERING THEIR OWN TRAPS.

11

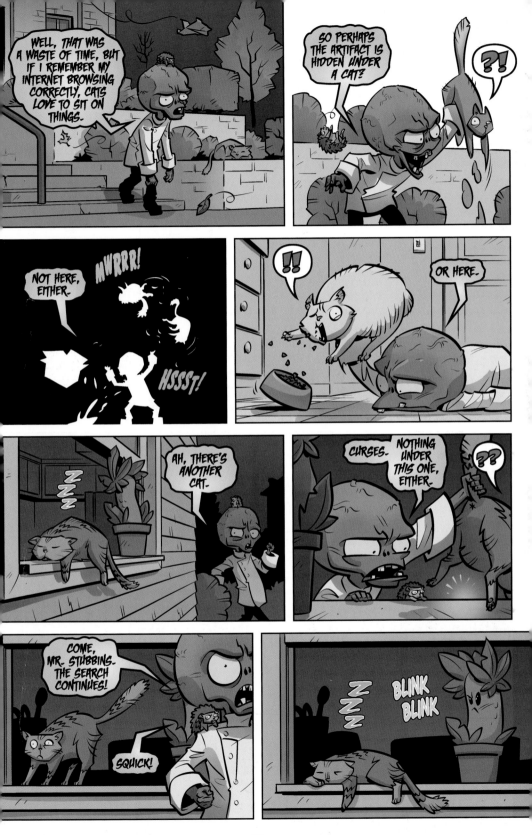

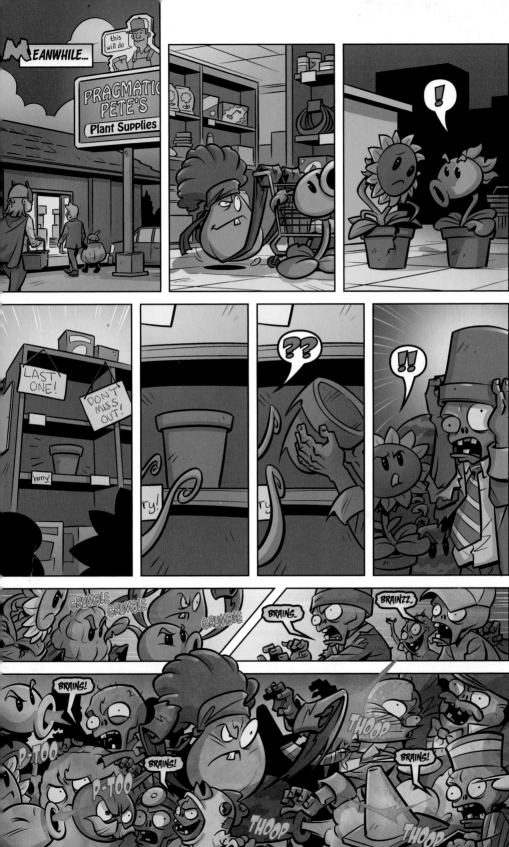

GUZZLE

GUZZLE

GUZZLE

FWOOOP!!

P-THOOM!

P-THOOM!

P-THOOM!

BOOM!

BAMM!

B-TOOM

BRAAAINS!

Costume Contest!

SHARK-ENSTEIN COSTUME!

IMPARTIAL JUDGE!

5

GHOST TOASTER!

6

SHAVED WEREWOLF!

7

Middle-Aged Parents With Children!

4

human child

human child

Adventure COMIC BOOK!

WOOO BOY Adventure

Sir Reginald Percy Fartwhistle vs GHOST TOASTERS!

8

SCUBA DIVER IN JAM JAR!

8

Costume Making Contest!

SEW!

SEW! SEW!

SEW! SEW!

SNIP!

SNIP! SNIP!

SNIP! SNIP!

SEW!

SNIP!

SEW!

SNIP!

Glitter!

ULTIMATE SPACE PRINCESS FACE-PUNCHER!!!

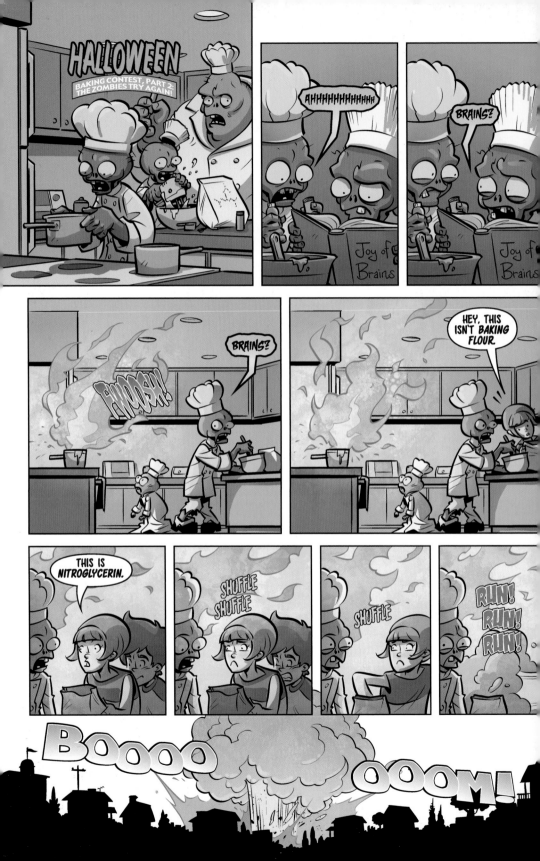

MEANWHILE, THE ZOMBIES ARE ENJOYING THE ONE NIGHT OF THE YEAR THEY CAN STROLL THE STREETS!

CINEMA

MY HOME: YOUR GRAVE! IN 3D!

OOO...I LIKED WHEN THE ZOMBIES WERE SAYING, "BRAINS! BRAINS!"

BRAINS! BRAINS!

HA HA HA! EXACTLY!

AND SOON...

KNOCK KNOCK!

OH, HELLO BOYS! LOVE YOUR COSTUMES! SO WELL DONE!

POUR POUR CANDY CANDY

54

SQUICK!!!

WRRR WRRR

SQUICK!!!

BRAAAAINS.

WRRR WRRR

SQUICK!!!
SQUICK!!!
SQUICK!!!

WRRR WRRR

BURBLE

GURGLE BLOOP

SQUICK!!!

WRRR WRRR

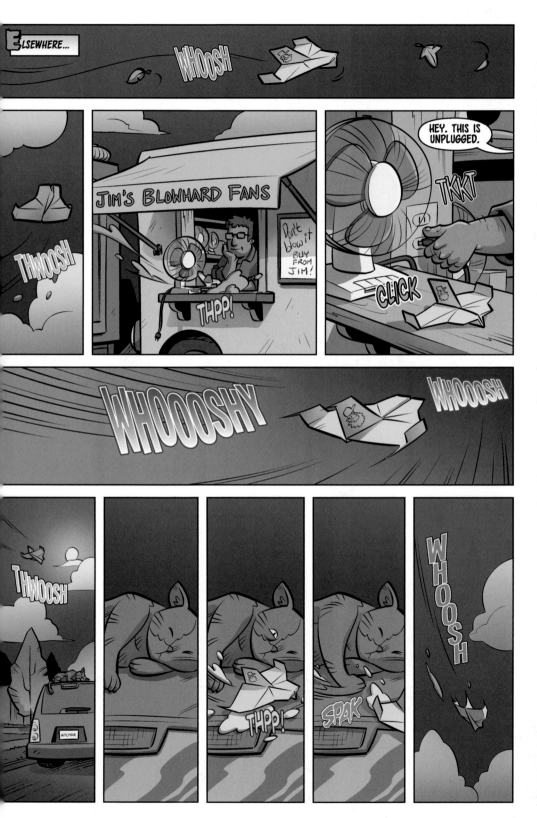

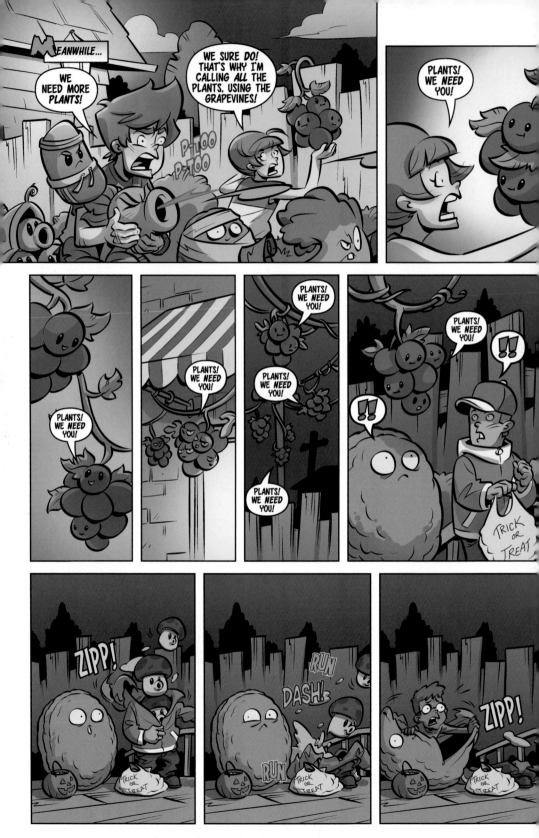

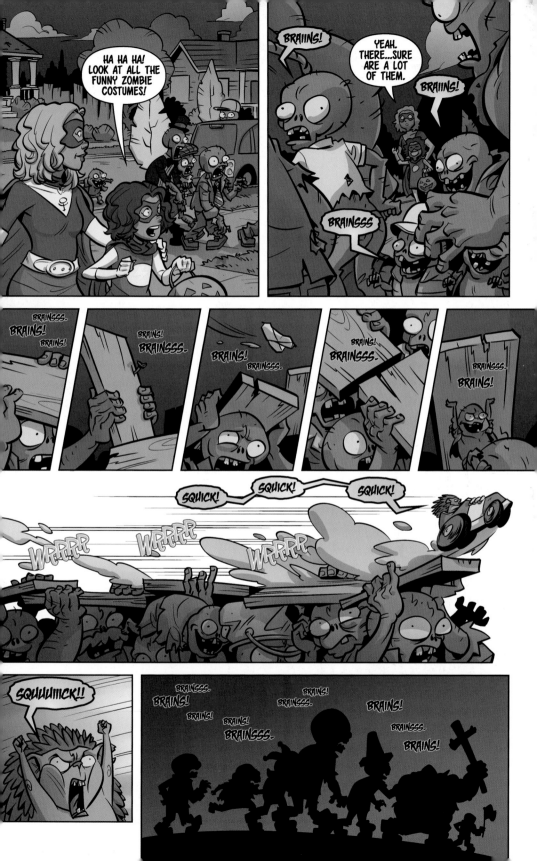

TIMEOUT FOR *SIX* DAYS!

YEAH. DIDN'T THINK THAT WOULD WORK.

B-TOOOM!

DODGE

IT'S NO USE, GUYS!

P-TOO P-TOO

THOOP THOOP

FLOONG!

THWORK!

GRAB NATE AND LET'S GET OUT OF HERE!

QUICK! THROUGH THIS YARD!

CLICK

UH-OH.

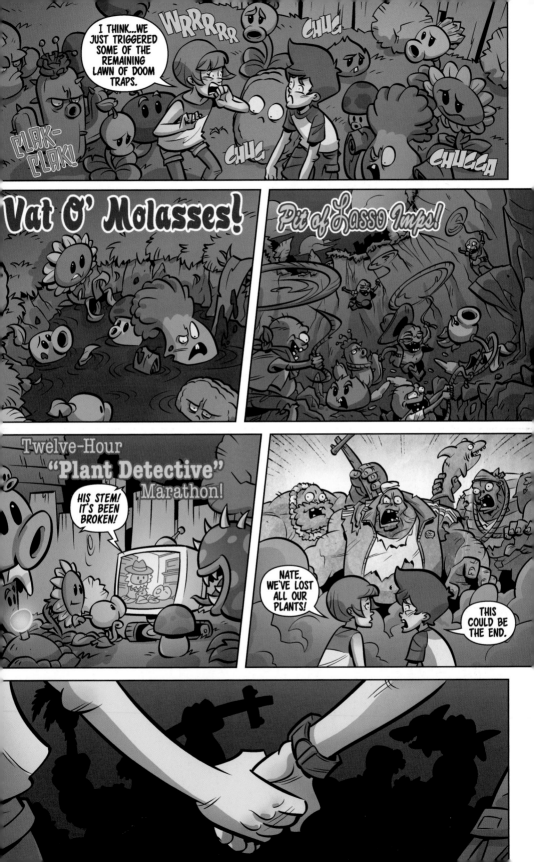

66

GLEAM!

HA!!!

KRACKA-BOOM!

HA! WE SURVIVED THANKS TO THE WISDOM OF THE TURTLES!

THANKS, TURTLE!

TERRIFIC TURTLE TRANSLATOR!

NO PROBLEM!

PLANTS VS. ZOMBIES:
LAWN OF DOOM
cover pencils by RON CHAN

CREATOR BIOS

Paul Tobin

Ron Chan

PAUL TOBIN enjoys that his author photo makes him look insane, and he once accidentally cut his ear with a potato chip. He doesn't know how it happened, either. Life is so full of mystery. If you ask him about the Potato Chip Incident, he'll just make up a story. That's what he does. He's written hundreds of stories for Marvel, DC, Dark Horse, and many others, including such creator-owned titles as *Colder* and *Bandette*, as well as *Prepare to Die!*—his debut novel. His *Genius Factor* series of novels about a fifth-grade genius and his war against the Red Death Tea Society debuted in March 2016 with *How to Capture an Invisible Cat*, from Bloomsbury Publishing, and continued in early 2017 with *How to Outsmart a Billion Robot Bees*. Paul has won some Very Important Awards for his writing but so far none for his karaoke skills.

RON CHAN is a comic book and storyboard artist, video game fan, and occasional jujitsu practitioner. He was born and raised in Portland, Oregon, where he still lives and works as a member of the local artist collective Helioscope. His comics work has been published by Dark Horse, Marvel, and Image Comics, and his storyboarding work includes boards for 3D animation, gaming, user-experience design, and advertising for clients such as Microsoft, Amazon Kindle, Nike, and Sega. He really likes drawing Bonk Choys. (He also enjoys eating actual bok choy in real life.)

Matt J. Rainwater

Steve Dutro

Residing in the cool, damp forests of Portland, Oregon, **MATT J. RAINWATER** is a freelance illustrator whose work has been featured in advertising, web design, and independent video games. On top of this, he also self-publishes several comic books, including *Trailer Park Warlock*, *Garage Raja*, and *The Feeling Is Multiplied*—all of which can be found at MattJRainwater.com. His favorite zombie-bashing strategy utilizes a line of Bonk Choys with a Wall-nut front guard and Threepeater covering fire.

STEVE DUTRO is an Eisner Award-nominated comic-book letterer from Redding, California, who can also drive a tractor. He graduated from the Kubert School and has been lettering comics since the days when foil-embossed covers were cool, working for Dark Horse (*The Fifth Beatle*, *I Am a Hero*, *Planet of the Apes*, *Star Wars*), Viz, Marvel, and DC. He has submitted a request to the Department of Homeland Security that in the event of a zombie apocalypse he be put in charge of all digital freeway signs so citizens can be alerted to avoid nearby brain-eatings and the like. He finds the *Plants vs. Zombies* game to be a real stress-fest, but highly recommends the *Plants vs. Zombies* table on *Pinball FX2* for game-room hipsters.

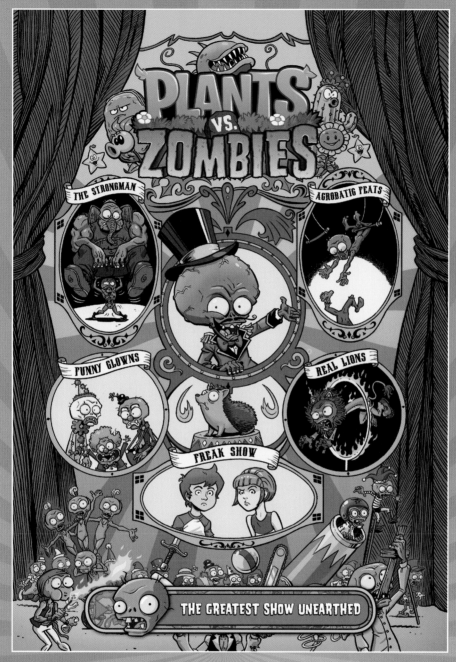

PLANTS VS. ZOMBIES: THE GREATEST SHOW UNEARTHED COMING TO TOWN FEBRUARY 2018!

Dr. Zomboss thinks that all humans hold a secret desire to run away and join the circus, so he aims to use his newly created Big Z's Adequately Amazing Flytrap Circus to lure Neighborville's citizens to their doom! Once plant-friendly neighborhood defenders Nate and Patrice infiltrate his show, though, Ringmaster Zomboss and his hapless zombies are in for a garden-ful of trouble!